Scott Foresman - Addison Wesley

Teacher's Toolkit

Kindergarten

Scott Foresman - Addison Wesley

Editorial Offices: Menlo Park, California • Glenview, Illinois
Sales Offices: Reading, Massachusetts • Atlanta, Georgia • Glenview, Illinois
Carrollton, Texas • Menlo Park, California

http://www.sf.aw.com

Overview

Teacher's Toolkit provides a collection of masters, transparencies, and management resources to assist with classroom management.

Classroom management resources provide suggestions for incorporating language skills into mathematics, providing cooperative learning experiences, and utilizing additional teaching strategies. Copies of the one-page lesson plan can assist in lesson preparation, while copies of the certificates of success can be awarded to recognize students' exceptional efforts and successes. A complete vocabulary list of all the words introduced in the *Student's Edition* is included, as is the entire student literature bibliography listed in the *Teacher's Edition.*

Teaching Tool Masters can be copied to provide students with mats, ten-frames, spinners, and other tools to assist their learning. Masters are referenced in the *Teacher's Edition* for use with specific lessons, although they may be useful in other situations as well.

Teaching Tool Transparencies include tools, gameboards, maps, and other materials referred to in the *Teacher's Edition.* Many of the sheets that accompany these transparencies can be copied and used by students to facilitate learning.

ISBN 0–201–31384–7

Copyright © Addison Wesley Longman, Inc.

All rights reserved.

Printed in the United States of America

7 8 9 10 – VSI – 02 01 00

© Scott Foresman Addison Wesley K

Table of Contents

Using Classroom Management Resources

There are several types of management resources available in the *Teacher's Toolkit*. Each resource offers options for you to use in meeting students' diversified needs.

English Language Development

This section provides general strategies that a teacher can use to help students who are not yet proficient in the English language.

Strategies for Teaching Vocabulary

This section provides guidance for effective vocabulary instruction and suggests vocabulary activities that use a variety of approaches and materials.

Cooperative Learning

This section provides the teacher with ways to maximize student learning when structuring activities that involve students working together as a team.

Additional Teaching Strategies

This section explores different teaching strategies that a teacher can use while working with students who are visually impaired, learning disabled, and so on.

Lesson Planner

This page can be used by the teacher to plan what he or she will do the next day in class. This tool can be prepared in advance and becomes invaluable to a substitute teacher when the teacher is absent.

Certificates of Success

These certificates can be used by the teacher as recognition of good and excellent progress by students in mathematics.

Vocabulary Lists

The vocabulary list is compiled by chapter. In Kindergarten, each vocabulary word is keyed to the lesson where it is used. In grades 1–8, each word is keyed to the page number where it is introduced.

Literature Bibliography

The two-page section provides a list of articles and books. The books are compiled by chapter and are related to the math content.

Classroom Management Resources

Classroom Management Resources

English Language Development

Students learning English as a second language (ESL) may need more time to make connections between concepts and mathematical language than other students. Most of these students are capable of performing work at their grade level and want to succeed in school, but their difficulty in communicating and the resulting problems often overwhelms and frustrates them.

Teachers who want to encourage growth and learning for these students are encouraged to draw upon what students already know and provide many opportunities for students to listen, speak, and write within these parameters. It is important that teachers use new terms frequently and encourage students to define mathematical terms in their own words.

Here are some general strategies that the teacher can use to help ESL students.

Provide a positive learning environment.

Make sure that students are comfortable enough to risk speaking and communicating in English without feeling ashamed if they are not always on target with the "correct" word or phrase. Emphasize communication, not English word and sentence structure.

Use manipulatives.

Manipulatives, such as place-value blocks, can be used to model mathematical concepts. Encourage students to describe the models using their own words. Other concrete approaches, such as pantomime and role-playing, may also be used when presenting new content.

Encourage both observation and participation.

Although one needs to encourage observation and participation, the teacher needs to be aware that the beginning language learner often goes through a period of limited participation. This is a learning period and does not indicate a lack of interest unless it continues for a long period of time. Therefore, the teacher should not force participation but wait until the student is comfortable enough to participate willingly in discussions. One way to elicit responses from these students is to ask questions that enable students to respond in nonverbal ways as well as in verbal ways. Thus, students do not feel threatened by their lack of command of the English language.

Encourage students to create visual displays.

It is especially important to encourage students to create visual displays when answering questions and when illustrating mathematical concepts. Have the students label the pictures with the appropriate symbols and words. This reinforces both the mathematical concept and the English terms used in relation with the concept.

Emphasize other cultures.

Create opportunities for students to use examples of mathematics from other cultures. Encourage students to make up their own problems that are rooted in familiar cultural perspectives.

Avoid rote or repetitive assignments.

Use assignments that stimulate students' thinking as they build their language skills. Encourage students to think critically and provide many activities that encourage creativity. It is especially important that teachers do not isolate students through excessive special assignments.

Emphasize cooperative learning.

Provide cooperative learning activities. Depending on the activities involved, teachers may want to team ESL students with others of similar backgrounds to generate a sense of camaraderie as both pursue a common goal. For other activities, teachers may wish to team ESL students with English-proficient students to further develop students' language skills.

At other times, teachers may want to use small group activities. Students often feel less pressured when working in a group and are more likely to take risks in this type of situation. Small group activities provide an atmosphere that fosters a natural situation in which students acquire language skills as well as building mathematical concepts.

Use paraphrasing and synonyms.

Build in reinforcement of English words with repetition, paraphrasing, and the use of synonyms. When speaking, use shorter sentences and repeat the concept in several different ways. This will reduce the pressure of using and understanding more complex sentence construction. During question-and-answer periods, allow students extra time to decode English words and make the appropriate calculations before they respond.

Explore multiple meanings of words.

When using vocabulary words that have more than one meaning, take time to explore each meaning and how it applies to the current situation. For example, a word such as *operation* can mean something that happens in a hospital or something one does with numbers. Elicit from students which meaning is appropriate to use in the current situation.

Accept all valid responses.

Accept a variety of responses as valid means of communication. For example, a student may choose to answer with gestures or make an attempt to act it out. Allowing the use of body language as a response can help the ESL students clarify the concept. Reinforce the concept by summarizing the response in English.

For example, when a student responds to the question "What figure has 4 sides and 4 right angles?" by drawing a square, you may wish to point to the picture and say, "Yes, a square is one figure that has 4 sides and 4 right angles."

Provide positive feedback.

Always try to model correct language usage for students rather than constantly correcting students' grammatical errors.

Always praise a student when he or she achieves success. If a sentence is incomplete or contains grammatical errors but the concept is correct, reinforce the student's attempt by saying "That's right." and then repeating the sentence correctly.

Monitor students' progress.

Review students' work frequently. Adjust instruction as needed.

Provide materials for bilingual students.

It is important to have an abundance of dictionaries, glossaries, and visual materials for students to use in the classroom.

Additional tips for teaching ESL students that relate directly to the lesson can be found in the Teacher's Edition. *Teaching Tool Transparencies* keyed to specific lessons ensure that these students' needs can be met using materials developed specifically for this elementary program.

Strategies for Teaching Vocabulary

It is essential that students gain proficiency in the vocabulary presented in the context of each lesson. Whenever possible, you can use visual aids, diagrams or pictures, and concrete objects when introducing new vocabulary words to help students visualize the meaning of the new word. Give special emphasis to vocabulary that is confusing for students with language or reading difficulties.

Introducing math vocabulary

All students are first introduced to new math vocabulary as the teacher guides them through the initial teaching steps for a lesson. Students in grades 3–8 also have the vocabulary words and definitions listed under Vocabulary on the pupil page in the lesson where it appears, and each new word is highlighted in the actual lesson where it is first used. All vocabulary words used at your grade level are listed in the *Vocabulary Lists* in this section.

When introducing new vocabulary words, it is important to introduce only one word at a time. Write the word on the chalkboard. Then say the word aloud and have students repeat it. This procedure often helps students fix the word in their minds, although it does little to reinforce the meaning. To do this, teachers can provide a real-world example that illustrates the word and allows students to relate it to their own prior experiences.

Example: Suppose the teacher needs to introduce the word *fraction*.

1. Write some fractions on the chalkboard.

2. Point to the fractions on the chalkboard and say, "These are examples of some fractions. Fractions can name a part of a whole."

3. Have students repeat the word.

4. Create a real-world situation, such as cutting an orange in half, that illustrates the word. To reinforce the meaning of the word, bring a real orange to class and demonstrate.

5. Have students use clay to make pseudo oranges and cut each of them in half.

Introducing non-math vocabulary

An unfamiliar word may sometimes be used in the student text. If the meaning of such a word is not addressed by the teacher at the beginning of the lesson, the student may have difficulty in completing the assignment. The teacher may wish to use the pictures in the student book to reinforce the word and its meaning. If none are available, you may wish to bring some pictures to the classroom, draw a diagram, or have students act it out.

Example: Suppose the teacher needs to introduce the word *dinosaur*.

1. Hold up the picture or a model.

2. Point to the picture or model and say, "This is a dinosaur."

3. Have students repeat the word.

4. Use the word in several short sentences, such as "The dinosaur is a very large animal. The dinosaur lived long ago."

5. Hold up another picture or model of a dinosaur and ask the class to identify it.

6. Ask volunteers to use the word in a sentence.

7. Be positive and upbeat. Allow students many opportunities to communicate and use the new vocabulary.

Teaching and reinforcing vocabulary

Teaching and reinforcing vocabulary is as important as introducing the new words. A teacher can use various methods to reinforce vocabulary introduced in any math lesson.

Example: Suppose students have just been introduced to *regroup*.

1. Encourage students to write a definition for *regroup* in their journal.

2. Have them write a sentence using *regroup*.

3. Ask them to draw a picture or a diagram that visually represents the meaning of *regroup*. Encourage them to write *regroup* underneath the picture or diagram.

4. Encourage all students to write a short story that uses *regroup* correctly.

Activities you can use to enhance and reinforce vocabulary learning

Flashcards Encourage students to make flashcards for new vocabulary words by writing the word on one side of the card and its definition on the other. They can then use the cards as repetitive practice to reinforce the word and its meaning. This could be done individually or in pairs.

Bulletin board Make a bulletin board display of important vocabulary words and use pictures as well as descriptions to match the words.

Learning center Have students use a tape recorder in the center to tape new words and their meanings. They can practice using the words in sentences. Then have them play their recordings back and edit their sentences if necessary.

Set up matching cards in the center. Encourage students to match the correct meanings to the correct vocabulary word.

Encourage students to use manipulatives contained in the center to represent vocabulary words whenever possible. Also have students use concrete examples to model new vocabulary words wherever applicable.

Play act When possible, have students write a skit using vocabulary words. Then let them perform the skit before other groups or classes.

Games you can use to enhance and reinforce vocabulary learning

Password (Five players) Students need paper and pencil and a stopwatch to play this game. Choose one player as the word giver. Form two teams of two players. The word giver writes the word on two slips of paper and gives the slip to a member of each team. That member gives a one-word clue to his or her teammate, and the teammate tries to guess the word. If the word is guessed, the team receives 10 points. If it is not guessed, the other team takes its turn. If the word is guessed, the team receives 9 points. If it is not guessed, the first team gets another chance with the value for guessing the word dropping to 8 points. This process is repeated until one team guesses the word. Play until one team reaches a set number of points, such as 50.

Categories (Two or more players) One person names a category, such as addition. The next player must name something that relates to addition, such as plus. Play continues until a player is stumped or uses a word that has already been named. This game is good to use for non-math words as well and encourages students to retrieve words from memory that may not be commonly used.

Words that make up a dollar! (Any number of players) Each player needs paper and pencil to play this game. Calculators and dictionaries may be helpful but are not essential to a student's success. Write the alphabet on the chalkboard and include the numbers below beside the letters.

A, 1	B, 2	C, 3	D, 4	E, 5	F, 6	G, 7
H, 8	I, 9	J, 10	K, 11	L, 12	M, 13	N, 14
O, 15	P, 16	Q, 17	R, 18	S, 19	T, 20	U, 21
V, 22	W, 23	X, 24	Y, 25	Z, 26		

Encourage players to find words whose letters add up exactly to 100. You may wish to have students compile a classroom list of all the dollar words they are able to find.

Cooperative Learning

When students work cooperatively, they become motivated, enthusiastic learners. The benefits of cooperative learning include improved attitudes toward school, increased powers of retention, and greater sensitivity to the interest and needs of others. The basis of cooperative learning is positive interdependence; the approach goes beyond simply telling students to work in pairs or groups. Rather, cooperative learning is an experience through which students realize that they are united in a common endeavor; that they will succeed or fail as a team. Besides interdependence, cooperative learning fosters individual accountability—students understand that they are each responsible for learning the content of the lessons.

Forming an effective cooperative learning group involves more that just putting students together in small groups and giving them a problem to solve. The teacher must give careful attention to the needs of the students in order to elicit the most benefits from the process. The teacher can facilitate learning in cooperative groups by

- deciding whether to place students in random or heterogeneous groups.
- modeling appropriate social skills, such as ways to offer encouragement and help to another member of the group.
- rearranging the classroom so that students have ample space to work without distracting other groups.
- making sure that the students know what they are going to do, why they are going to do it, and how they are expected to work.

Choose lessons for cooperative learning activities that have many possible answers and allow students to choose from many different strategies when solving the problem. Be sure to allow adequate time for summarizing so that groups have an opportunity to share their solutions and questions. The resulting discussion can lead them to generalize from the specific problem by looking for patterns or relationships in the data.

How to Use Cooperative Learning Groups

Some teachers place students in groups to check math homework and reach a common solution to each problem. This approach works best when each student has completed the homework assignment.

Other teachers use small groups as a follow-up to whole-group instruction. Students in each group work on problems related to the lesson. By giving students an opportunity to apply newly-learned skills to a real-world situation, the teacher reinforces the learning that has taken place.

Yet other teachers use small groups as the way to develop the lesson itself. In this situation, the students, as a team, work through the problem or activity at their own pace and the group reaches a consensus on the answer or answers to the problem.

Developing Necessary Social Skills

Encourage students to develop the following social skills so that students can work together in a friendly fashion and focus on the problem at hand. The teacher may want to post these rules on the bulletin board so that students can easily refer to them.

Basic classroom rules
- Listen to what other have to say.
- Respect others and their ideas.
- Take your responsibilities seriously.
- Stick to the task at hand.

Actions of a cooperative group member
- Stays with the group, speaks quietly, and shares materials.
- Addresses others by name, looks at the person speaking, and encourages others to participate.
- Looks at the group's work and contributes ideas.
- Allows each person to respond before speaking again.

Actions of an effective group member
- Criticizes ideas without criticizing people.
- States the differences when there is a disagreement.
- Pulls together all the ideas into a single position.
- Asks others to verbalize how they would solve a problem or reach a decision.
- Asks people to explain their reasoning.
- Seeks elaboration by referring to other learning or knowledge.
- Builds on others' ideas.
- Listens to all ideas before reaching a conclusion.

How to Set Up a Cooperative Learning Group

Sometimes the teacher may need to assign roles to group members. Other times, the teacher may let students choose the roles they will play in solving the problem. These roles can include the following.

Reader: The reader reads the problem to the groups and makes sure every group member understands what he or she is to do. The reader makes sure that the group as a whole stays on task.

Materials manager: The materials manager gathers all the materials needed to complete the activity–paper, blocks, cubes, play money, graph paper, and so on. The manager is also responsible for cleaning up the work area and returning any unused materials.

Recorder: The recorder takes notes as the group completes the task or solves the problem. The recorder reviews his or her notes, and writes the answer or conclusions in a final form to be given to the reader or reporter.

Calculator: The calculator does the computation necessary to complete the task.

Checker: The checker checks the group's work or answers before turning over the work to the reporter or teacher.

Reporter: The reporter summarizes the group's work for the class or teacher and reports the answers and turns in the group's work to the teacher.

Every student should have the opportunity to play each role at different times during the year. You may want to prepare a set of posters that name and describe each role. Keep the posters visible during cooperative learning activities.

Additional Teaching Strategies

There are several teaching strategies the teacher can use when teaching mathematics. Some of these strategies are shown below. Often, strategies are combined or seem to overlap. For instance, the example given when using manipulatives and modeling also requires students to act out the problem to find a solution.

Encouraging student conversation

When students work in cooperative learning situations, encourage them to talk with each other about the tasks they perform. Encourage communication by asking students to describe what they are doing and explain why. A teacher may need to guide students in this type of interaction.

Example: Suppose students are studying addition and subtraction.

Ask Jorge to tell Linda why he removed a piece from a model he made.

As the teacher listens to the conversations, he or she will be better able to decide what these students know and do not know. It is all right for students to disagree as long as they disagree about issues and do not let it escalate in disagreements between personalities. Disagreements that focus on issues can often open the door to higher-level thinking skills and provide ample opportunities for language use.

Using gestures

Using gestures can facilitate understanding. For example, when you are referring to an object, you may wish to focus students' attention on the object by holding it up for students to see or pointing to it in the classroom. Encourage students to use gestures whenever they have difficulty communicating in words.

Example 1: Which of these basic facts are correct?

Prepare several fact cards, some with incorrect answers. Have students respond with thumbs up when the fact shown is correct and with thumbs down when the fact shown is incorrect.

Example 2: About how long is an inch? A foot? A yard?

Ask students to practice holding their hands about 1 inch apart, 1 foot apart, and 1 yard apart. Then ask them to raise their hands when they think a minute has passed. These activities will help students gain a concrete understanding of units of measure.

Using manipulatives and modeling

The importance of using manipulatives when teaching concepts has been documented by extensive research. Manipulatives are tools that enable the teacher to provide multisensory learning experiences as the teacher models concepts. Manipulatives can also be used to reinforce concepts after they have been introduced. These learning experiences provide the foundation upon which students build as they move toward a greater level of abstraction.

Example 1: Carrie has 4 oranges and wants to share them equally with Maria. How many oranges will each girl get?

Encourage students to use counters to figure out how many oranges each girl will receive.

Example 2: Several cardboard triangles in different shapes are randomly mixed so that they may be turned or flipped. Have students match each triangle with another triangle in the group.

Be sure students understand that they may need to look for turned or flipped shapes in order to make all the matches.

Example 3: Give students exactly 18 counters and have them estimate how many there are. Then have students count the objects and record the actual number.

Let students work in pairs as they count and tally the counters. Encourage them to verbalize or write how they can find the total amount.

A teacher can use modeling to introduce a concept, such as regrouping sums. Often a student who is not English proficient will be able to understand quite well what is going on with the model. Having students model a concept can also be used to reinforce the concept once it is taught.

Example: Carmen and Jennie slide down one water slide. Eric slides down another water slide. How many students slide down the water slides?

Have students use counters to represent each student and pretend they are going down a slide. Slide two counters from an area designated as the top of the slide to an area designated as the bottom of the slide. Do the same thing with the other counter. Then ask students how many counters are at the bottom of the slide? Be sure they understand how their answer relates to the actual problem.

Acting out

Encourage students to act out a problem when confronted with a situation they cannot resolve. Acting out a problem actively involves students in the learning process. This method can be used to both introduce and reinforce concepts.

Example: May is sitting in the middle of a group of students on a park bench. There are 3 people on her right. How many people are sitting on the bench?

Encourage students to recreate the problem by having a student that represents May stand in a row. Then have 3 students stand on her right. Since she is in the middle, have another 3 students stand on her left. Then count the number of students in all. Another strategy students could use is Draw a Diagram.

Helping visually-impaired students learn

Different strategies need to be used to serve the needs of visually-impaired students. Type size on many of the learning materials may need to be larger so that students can focus on content without being distracted by his or her inability to see the words. For example, graphs need to be labeled clearly with large type so that students can read the scale on the graph. In other cases, objects can be made larger for the same reason.

Example: Is it likely or unlikely that you will draw a red marble?

Make sure that the jar is filled with marbles or other objects of distinctly different sizes and shapes to perform probability experiments.

Writing answers and problems

Encourage students to use their journal to write about what they learned in math that day as well as write answers to the Journal problems in the student book. Doing this helps students clarify their thinking and imprint in their mind the actual process they used to find the answer. Writing problems also builds students' language skills and demonstrates the underlying math understanding of the problem.

Example 1: Suppose you toss a number cube with sides labeled from 1 through 6 fifty times. Predict how many outcomes would be odd numbers. Explain your prediction.

Have students write the explanation in their journal and explain the process they used to decide upon their answers.

Example 2: Write a real-world problem that shows the joining of two sets of objects.

Encourage students to use complete sentences and correct terminology.

Lesson Planner

Teacher's Name _____   Date _____

Grade _____   M   T   W   Th   F

Lesson Objective _____

State/Local Objective _____

Lesson Resources

Blackline Masters

Practice Masters _____

Reteaching Masters _____

Enrichment Masters _____

Teaching Tool Masters _____

Technology Masters _____

Assessment Sourcebook _____

Teacher Resources/Materials

Teaching Tool Transparencies _____

Problem of the Day Flipchart _____

Big Book _____

Reading Strategies for Math _____

_____

_____

Student Resources/Materials

Crayons/markers _____   Calculator _____   _____

Grid paper _____   Colored paper _____   _____

Manipulatives _____   _____

Using the Calendar Time Kit

Calendar _____   Graphs _____

Time _____   Bundle Boxes _____

Money _____   Number Line _____

Adaptations

_____

_____

_____

Extensions

_____

_____

_____

Organizational Tips

_____

_____

_____

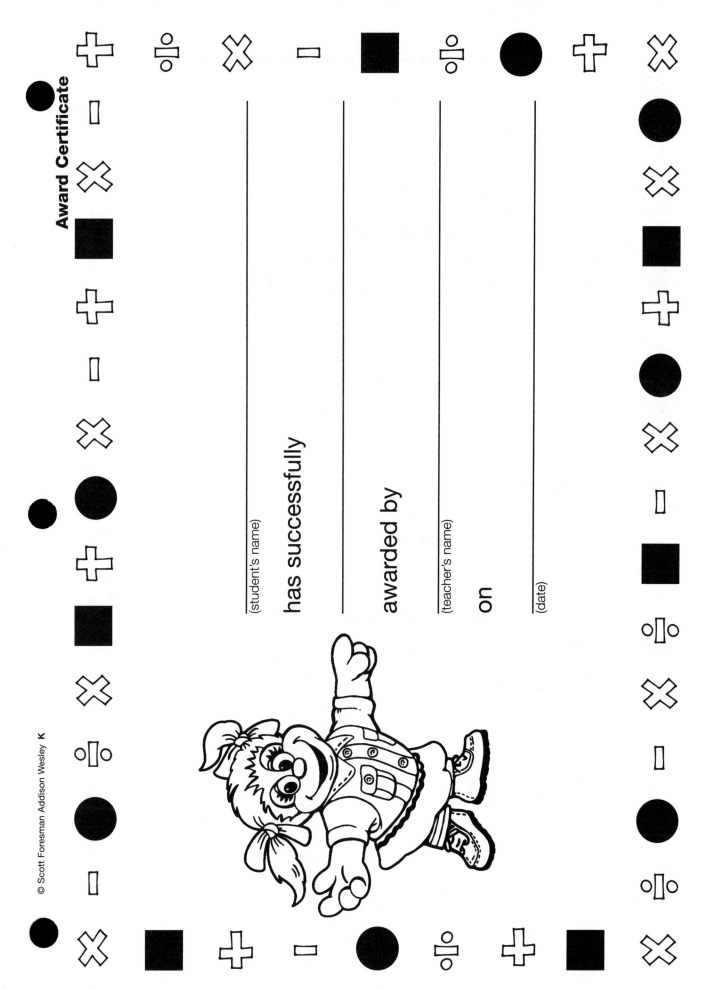

Award Certificate

_____
(student's name)

has successfully

_____

awarded by

_____
(teacher's name)

on

_____
(date)

Great work

(student's name)

YOU DID YOUR
Best in Math
TODAY!

awarded by

(teacher's name)

on

(date)

You Shared Some Great Ideas In Math Today!

(student's name)

awarded by

(teacher's name)

on

(date)

Nice try, _____
(student's name)

YOU REALLY TRIED HARD TODAY!

awarded by _____
(teacher's name)

on _____

_____
(date)

Great job, _____
(student's name)

You worked well with your Math Partner,

_____
(partner's name)

granted by _____
(teacher's name)

on _____
(date)

A FREEBIE!

Trade me in for

(student's name)

_____

Because of your

_____

from

(teacher's name)

on

(date)

Vocabulary Lists

Chapter 1	Lesson
top	1
middle	1
bottom	1
red	1
yellow	1
blue	1
over	1
between	1
under	1
above	2
below	2
over	2
between	2
under	2
before	3
after	3
between	3
over	3
under	3
left	4
right	4
inside	5
outside	5
attribute	6
color, size, and shape words	6
same	7
different	7
color	7
red	7
yellow	7
blue	7
green	7
orange	7
black	7
white	7
shape words (circle, oval, triangle, square, diamond, rectangle, star)	8
size words (big, little, medium)	8
same	9
different	9
size	9
shape	9
color	9

Chapter 2	Lesson
sort	1
sort	2
resort	2
as many as	3
more	4
fewer	4
less	4
sorting rule	5
real graph	6
more	6
less	6
fewer	6
as many as	6
most	6
least	6
picture graph	7
picture graph	8

Chapter 3	Lesson
pattern	1
pattern	2
first	2
next	2
before	2
after	2
last	2
pattern	3
pattern	4
pattern	5
same	5
alike	5
different	5
pattern	6
pattern	7
border	7
outside	7
inside	7
middle	7

Chapter 4	Lesson
one	1
two	1
three	1
one	2
two	2
three	3
four	4
five	4
four	5
five	6

zero	7
nothing	7
none	7
no	7
empty	7
group	8
same	8
more than	8
fewer than	8
sequence	9
smallest	9
biggest	9
order	10
compare	11
same	11
more	11
fewer	11
enough	12
more	12
fewer	12

Chapter 5	Lesson
six	1
seven	1
eight	1
six	2
seven	3
eight	4
nine	5
ten	5
nine	6
ten	7
one more	8
one less	8
one more	9
pattern	9
number order	10
before	10
after	10
more than	11
fewer than	11
equal (same as)	11
first	12
second	12
third	12
fourth	12
fifth	12
sixth	12
seventh	12
eighth	12

ninth	12
tenth	12
fewer than	13
more than	13

Chapter 6	Lesson
shorter	1
longer	1
taller	1
about the same	1
longer	2
shorter	2
about the same	2
more than	5
less than	5
about the same	5
holds	5
fill	5
empty	5
measure	6
capacity	6
about	6
weight	7
heavier than	7
lighter than	7
heavier	8
light	8
about the same	8

Chapter 7	Lesson
flat	1
smooth	1
round	1
tall	1
short	1
sharp	1
pointy	1
cylinder	2
cone	2
sphere	2
rectangular prism	2
pyramid	2
circle	3
triangle	3
rectangle	3
square	3
square	4
rectangle	4
sides	4
corners	4

circle	5
triangle	5
sides	5
corners	5
circle	6
square	6
rectangle	6
triangle	6
sides	6
corners	6
outline	7
equal	8
half	9
halves	9
equal groups	10
same	10
fair share	11

Chapter 8 — Lesson

ten-frame	1
one	1
two	1
three	1
four	1
five	1
six	1
seven	1
eight	1
nine	1
ten	1
three	2
four	2
five	3
six	3
seven	4
eight	4
nine	5
ten	5
pattern	6
eleven	7
twelve	7
thirteen	7
fourteen	7
fifteen	7
sixteen	7
seventeen	7
eighteen	7
nineteen	7
twenty	7
more than	8
less than	8
same as	8
fewer	8
estimate	8
more than	9

less than	9
same as	9
greater	9
fewer	9
almost	9
about	9
guess	9
estimate	9
legs	10

Chapter 9 — Lesson

before	1
after	1
first	2
next	2
last	2
clock	3
face	3
hands	3
hour	4
minute	4
time	4
digital	4
o'clock	4
hour hand	4
minute hand	4
list	5
penny	6
nickel	6
trade	6
cent	6
penny	7
nickel	7
cent	7
penny	8
dime	8
trade	8
costs more	9
costs less	9
trade	9
cost more	10
cost less	10
trade	10

Chapter 10 — Lesson

join	1
in all	1
length	2
long	2
join	2
in all	2
how many	2
take away	3
left	3
separate	3

length	4
long	4
take apart	4
left	4
how many	5
in all	5
take away	5
left	5
how many	6
more	6
fewer	6
compare	6
how many	7
longer	7
shorter	7
clues	8

Chapter 11 — Lesson

tens	1
extras	1
eleven	2
twelve	2
thirteen	2
fourteen	2
fifteen	2
sixteen	3
seventeen	3
eighteen	3
nineteen	3
estimate	4
check	4
twenty	5
twenty-one	5
twenty-two	5
twenty-three	5
twenty-four	5
twenty-five	5
twenty-six	5
twenty-seven	5
twenty-eight	5
twenty-nine	5
thirty	5
calendar	6
month	6
day	6
week	6
more	7
fewer	7
same	7
compare	7
length	8
capacity	8
long	8
about	8
holds	8

guess	8
check	8
measure	8
estimate	8
length	9
measure	9

Chapter 12 — Lesson

add	1
more	1
sum	1
joining	1
add	2
more	2
sum	2
joining	2
add	3
more	3
sum	3
joining	3
add	4
more	4
sum	4
joining	4
add	5
more	5
sum	5
joining	5
how many left	6
leave	7
how many left	7
six	7
seven	7
leave	8
how many left	8
eight	8
nine	8
minus	9
equals	9
ten	9
add	10
subtract	10
plus	10
minus	10
equal	10

Literature Bibliography (Grade K)

For each book below, an activity connecting the literature selection to specific math content appears in the Teacher's Edition on the Start-Up page of the lesson(s) listed. Many of these titles are available through Cuisenaire/Dale Seymour Publications. Call 1-800-237-3142.

Lesson	Book Title / Author / Publisher
1-5	*The Mitten* / Jan Brett /G.P. Putnam's Sons, 1989
1-6, 1-7, 1-8	*I Spy: A Book of Picture Riddles* / Jean Marzollo / Scholastic, 1992
1-8, 1-9	*Circles, Triangles, and Squares* / Tana Hoban / Simon and Schuster Books for Young Readers, 1974
2-3, 2-4	*One by One* / Judy Hindley / Candlewick Press, 1985
2-6, 2-7	*The Button Box* / Margarette S. Reid / Dutton Children's Books, 1990
3-1, 3-5	*To Bathe a Boa* / C. Imbior Kudrna / Carolrhoda Books, 1986
3-4, 3-5, 3-7	*Over in the Meadow* / Ezra Jack Keats / Four Winds Press, 1971
4-1, 4-4, 4-10	*Ten Black Dots* / Donald Crews / Greenwillow Books, 1986
4-4, 4-10	*The Very Hungry Caterpillar* / Eric Carle / Putnam, 1969
4-7, 4-9, 4-10	*Anno's Counting Book* / Mitsumasa Anno / Harper, 1977
4-9, 4-10	*One by One* / Judy Hindley / Candlewick Press, 1996
5-1	*The Napping House* / Audrey Wood / Harcourt Brace, 1984
5-3, 5-12	*Seven Blind Mice* / Ed Young / Philomel, 1992
5-6, 5-9	*Emeka's Gift* / Ifeoma Onyefulu / Cobblehill Books, 1995
5-8, 5-11	*Five Little Monkeys Jumping on the Bed* / Eileen Christelow / Clarion Books, 1989
6-1	*Big Friend, Little Friend* / Eloise Greenfield / Black Butterfly Children's Books, 1991
6-4	*How Big is a Foot?* / Rolf Myller / Dell Publishing, 1991
6-7	*Just a Little Bit* / Ann Tompert / Houghton Mifflin, 1993
6-9	*Peter's Pockets* / Eve Rice / Greenwillow Books, 1989
7-3, 7-4, 7-5	*Shapes, Shapes, Shapes* / Tana Hoban / Greenwillow Books, 1986
7-8, 7-9, 7-10	*Eating Fractions* / Bruce McMillan / Scholastic, 1991
7-9	*The Little Mouse, The Red Ripe Strawberry, and The Big Hungry Bear* / Don and Audrey Wood / Child's Play, 1996
8-1 to 8-5, 8-7	*Count and See* / Tana Hoban / Simon and Schuster, 1993
8-5	*A Number of Animals* / Kate Green / Creative Editions, 1993
8-6	*Ten Flashing Fireflies* / Philemon Sturges / North-South Books, 1995
8-7	*Bears and the Beach Counting 10 to 20* / Niki Yektai / Millbrook Press, 1996

Lesson	Book Title / Author / Publisher
9-1	*One Afternoon* / Yumi Heo / Orchard Books, 1994
9-4	*The Grouchy Ladybug* / Eric Carle / Harper, 1986
9-5	*Don't Forget the Bacon* / Pat Hutchins / Mulberry Books, 1976
9-10	*The Berenstain Bears' Trouble with Money* / Stan and Jan Berenstain / Random House, 1983
10-2	*Fish Eyes* / Lois Ehlert / Harcourt Brace, 1980
10-4	*Ten Little Mice* / Joyce Dunbar / Voyager Books, 1995
10-6	*The Twelve Days of Summer* / E. L. O'Donnell / Morrow Junior Books, 1991
11-1	*The Icky Bug Counting Book* / Jerry Pallotta / Charlesbridge Publishing, 1992
11-6	*Chicken Soup with Rice: A Book of Months* / Maurice Sendak / Harper Trophy, 1990
11-8	*Growing Vegetable Soup* / Lois Ehlert / Voyager Books, 1987
11-9	*Inch by Inch* / Leo Lionni / Mulberry Books, 1995
12-3 to 12-5	*One Gorilla* / Atsuko Morozumi / A Sunburst Book, 1990
12-4, 12-5, 12-10	*Mouse Party* / Alan Durant / Candlewick Press, 1995
12-6, 12-10	*Benny's Pennies* / Pat Brisson / Bantam Doubleday Dell, 1993
12-10	*Number One Number Fun* / Kay Chorao / Holiday House, 1995

© Scott Foresman Addison Wesley **K**

Using Teaching Tool Masters

Teachers have a variety of masters from which to choose in grades K–2. The masters often provide tools that may not be available in all classrooms, such as patterns for spinners in grades 1 and 2. They are designed to be used with specific lessons and are keyed to those lessons in the *Teacher's Edition.* However, the *Teaching Tool Masters,* such as the inch- and centimeter-rulers, often can be incorporated into other areas of math instruction as well.

Most of the masters enable the teacher to present mathematical concepts at the concrete level by providing manipulative tools for students to use.

> **Example:** Aids for teaching addition and subtraction appear in all three grades with masters specially earmarked for the child's maturity level and content level. You will find these masters at grades K-2 that relate specifically to addition and subtraction content strands.
>
> ### Kindergarten
> *Ten Frames for Addition*
> *Double Ten-Frame Recording Sheet*
> *Double Ten-Frame Flash Cards*
> *Addition Recording Sheet*
> *Subtraction Recording Sheet*
>
> ### Grade 1
> *Double 9 Dominoes*
> *6 Cubes That Add Up*
> *7 Cubes That Add Up*
> *Tens and Ones Mat*
> *Addition Facts Through 12*
> *Subtraction Facts Through 12*
> *Addition Facts Through 18*
> *Subtraction Facts Through 18*
>
> ### Grade 2
> *Double Circle Diagram*
> *Triple Circle Diagram*
> *What's My Rule? Tables*
> *Gameboards*
> *Addition Charts*
> *Subtraction Charts*

Still other masters provide teaching tools that accommodate the same solid foundation for math with a continued rise in the level of difficulty from grade to grade. See Table of Contents for a complete listing of masters.

Teaching Tool Masters

Teaching Tool Masters

● **Set of Shapes**

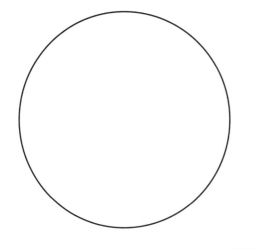
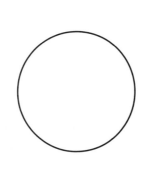
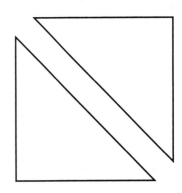

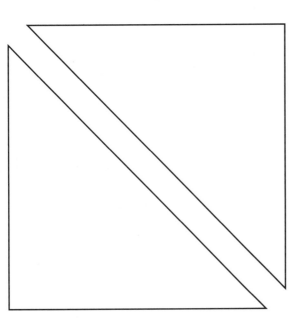
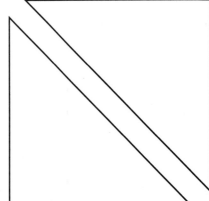

Ten Frames for Addition

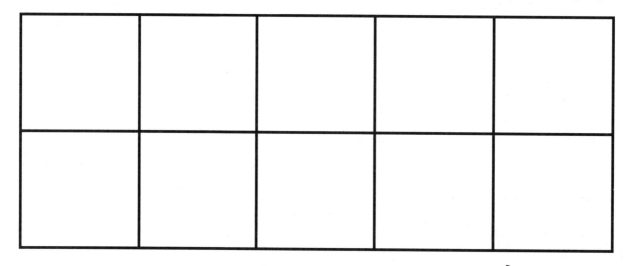

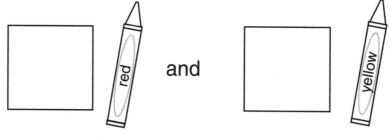

and

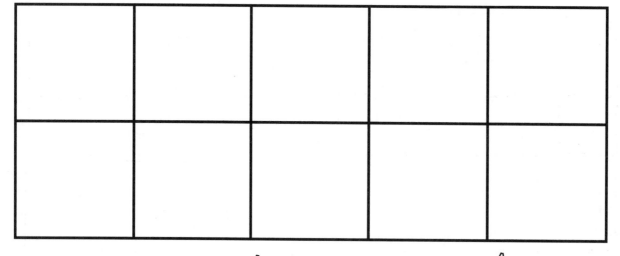

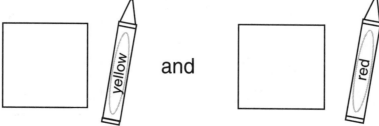

and

Name _____

Double Ten-Frame Recording Sheet

Name _____

Clock Face

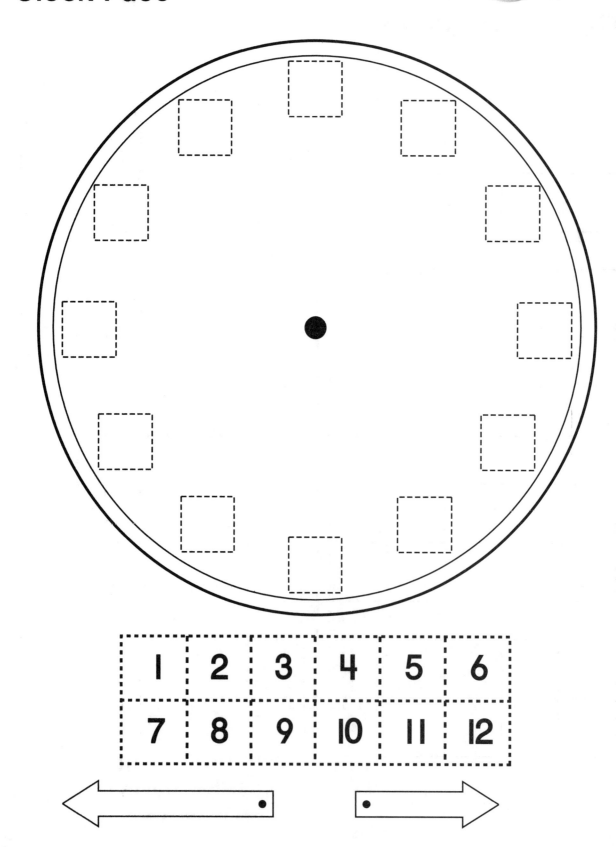

4

● Double Ten-Frame Flash Cards

Name _____

Footprint Cut-outs

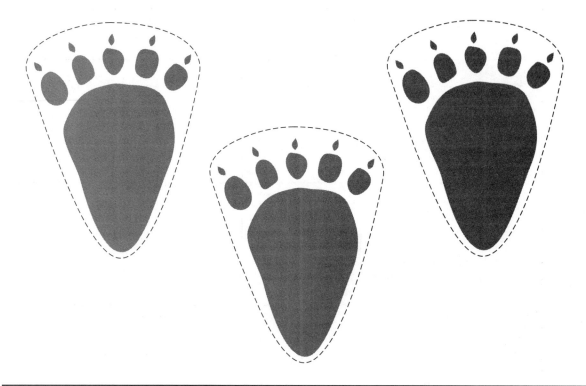

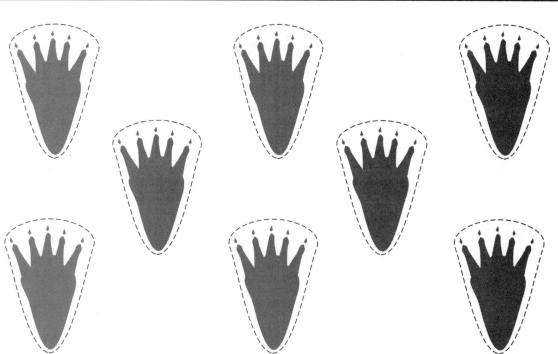

6

● **Addition Recording Sheet**

	and		is	
☐	and	☐	is	☐
☐	and	☐	is	☐
☐	and	☐	is	☐
☐	and	☐	is	☐
☐	and	☐	is	☐
☐	and	☐	is	☐
☐	and	☐	is	☐

Name _____

Subtraction Recording Sheet

☐ in all   ☐ leave   ☐ are left

☐ in all   ☐ leave   ☐ are left

☐ in all   ☐ leave   ☐ are left

☐ in all   ☐ leave   ☐ are left

☐ in all   ☐ leave   ☐ are left

☐ in all   ☐ leave   ☐ are left

☐ in all   ☐ leave   ☐ are left

Using Teaching Tool Transparencies

The *Teacher's Toolkit* offers a variety of transparencies. They are designed to be used with specific lessons and are keyed to those lessons in the *Teacher's Edition.* However, some *Teaching Tool Transparencies* can be incorporated into other areas of math instruction as well.

>**Example:** At grades 3–8, teachers are encouraged to use the Guided Problem Solving transparencies any time they work through word problems with the class and not just when problem-solving lessons are presented in the student book.

The *Teaching Tool Transparencies* provide a way to accommodate group discussion while maintaining a hands-on approach to learning. They allow the teacher to illustrate math concepts at a concrete level.

>**Example:** The teacher may model a math concept using a transparency while students imitate the model using manipulatives at their desks. Working at the concrete level along with the teacher helps build students' understanding of the concept being presented.

The sheets between the transparencies may be copied to provide students with identical tools, gameboards, or worksheets for independent or group work.

Teaching Tool Transparencies

Teaching Tool Transparencies

Ten Frame

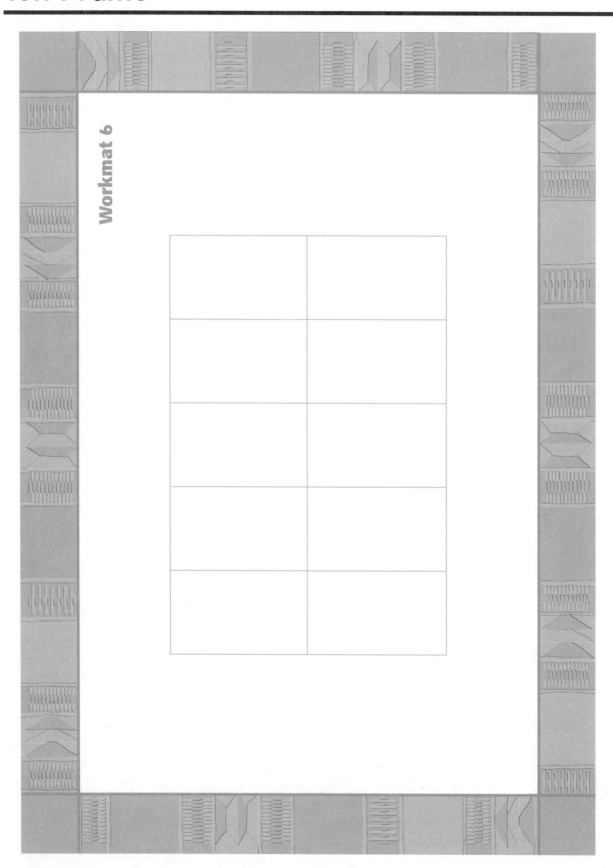

Workmat 6

2-Group Sorting Mat

Workmat 2

3-Group Sorting Mat

Workmat 4

2 × 10 Graphing Grid

Workmat 5

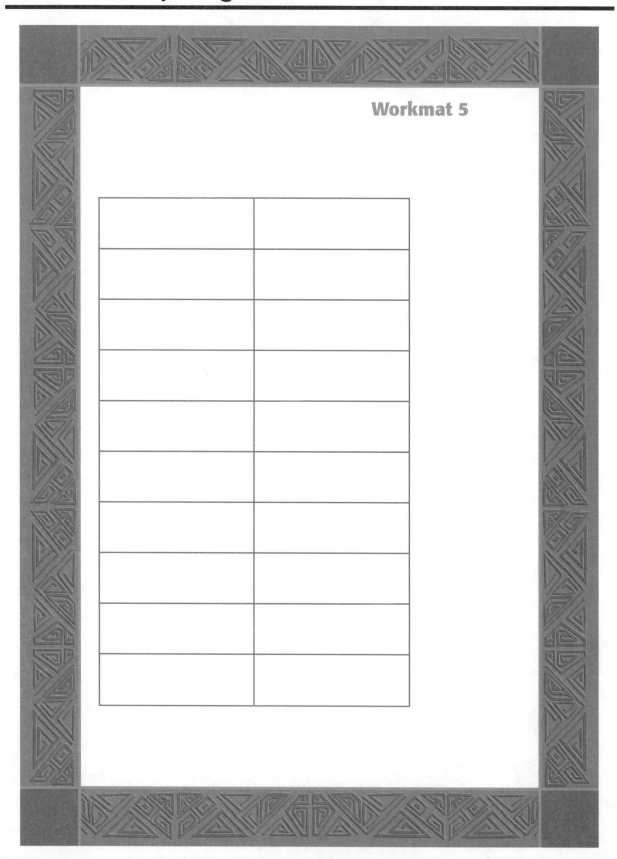

Graphing Grid (4 rows)

Snap™ Cubes

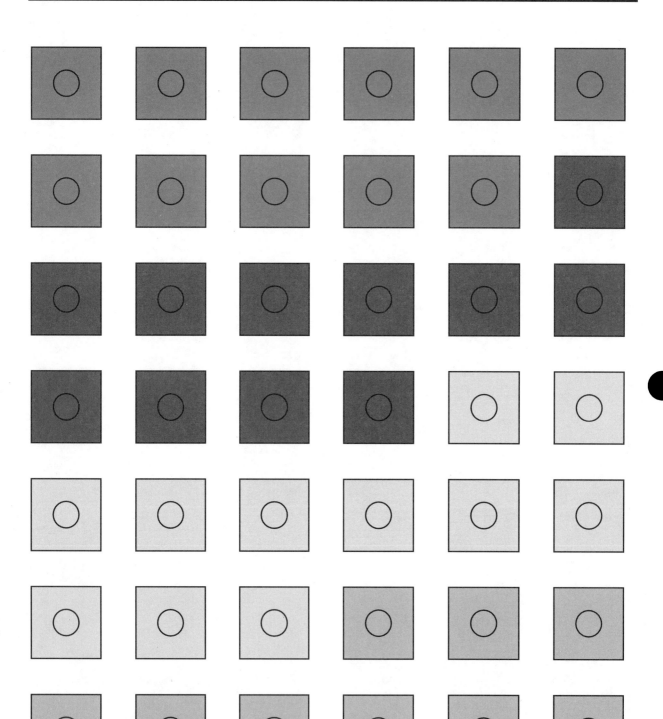

More Snap™ Cubes

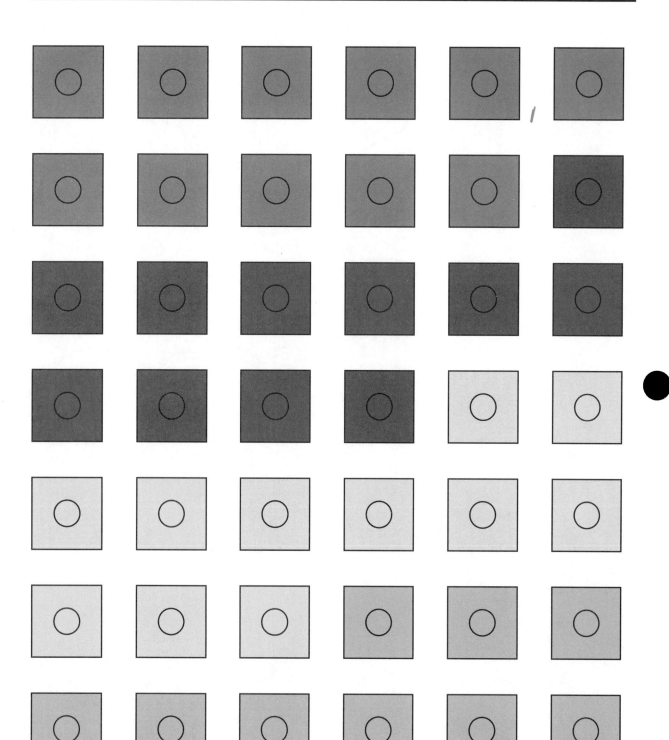

Number Cards (10–20)

10	11	12	13
14	15	16	17
18	19	20	

Number Cards (21–31)

21	22	23	24
25	26	27	28
29	30	31	

Double Ten Frame

Workmat 3

Calendar

Month:						
Sunday	Monday	Tuesday	Wednesday	Thursday	Friday	Saturday
						1
2	3	4	5	6	7	8
9	10	11	12	13	14	15
16	17	18	19	20	21	22
23	24	25	26	27	28	29
30	31					

2-Color Counters

Thermometer

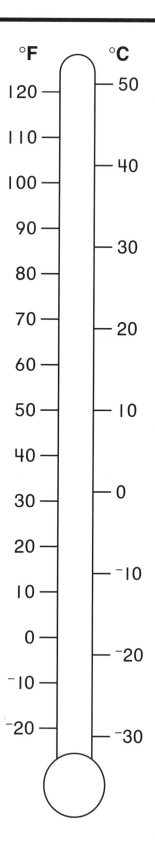

°F   °C

120 —   — 50

110 —

100 —   — 40

90 —

80 —   — 30

70 —   — 20

60 —

50 —   — 10

40 —

30 —   — 0

20 —

10 —   — ⁻10

0 —

⁻10 —   — ⁻20

⁻20 —   — ⁻30

Coins

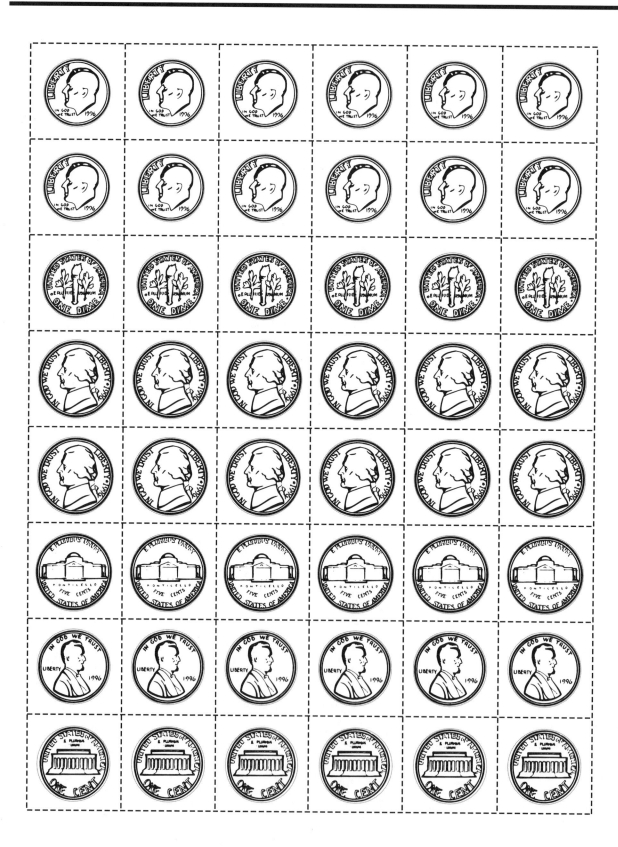

Blank Calendar

Month:						
Sunday	Monday	Tuesday	Wednesday	Thursday	Friday	Saturday

Clock

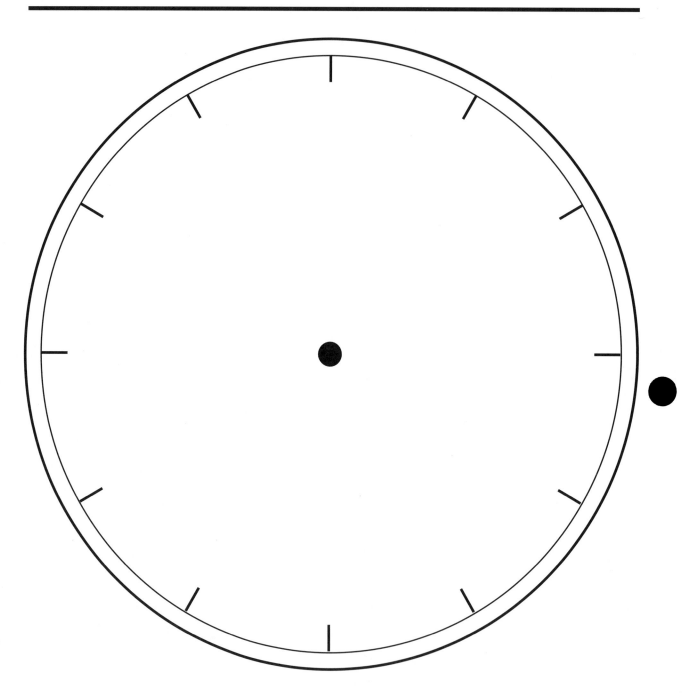